Preschool Workbook
Toddler Coloring Book
Math Practice Workbook
for Kids Ages 4-8

Trace Numbers

We create our workbooks with love and great care.
For any issues with your workbook, such as printing errors, typos, faulty binding, or something
else, please do not hesitate to contact us at: info@homerunpress.com.
We will make sure you get a replacement copy immediately.

THANK YOU!

First published in the USA 2020.   ISBN 9781952368073

Say the number. Trace the number. Write the number.

I see **0** bunnies.

zero

0 0 0 0 0 0

0 0 0 0 0 0

Follow the animals with your finger as they move across the page.
Then, draw a line with a red crayon.

Each item on the page has a twin. <u>Draw</u> a line to connect the twins!

Draw an X on the picture that does not belong in the group.

Say the number. Trace the number. Write the number.

I see   I   bunny.

Find the mystery house.

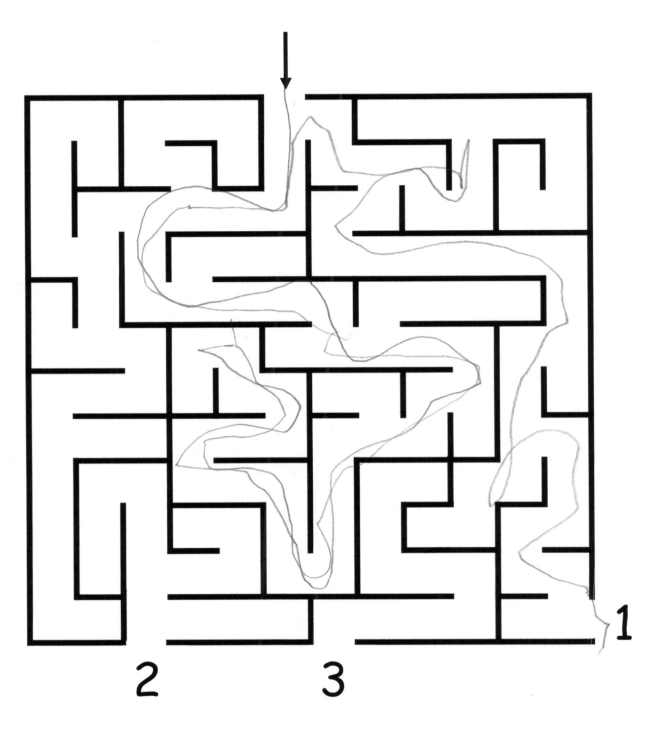

2   3

Circle the mystery house: 2   1   3

Follow the butterflies with your finger as they move across the page. Then, draw a line with a green crayon.

Count the objects. Write the number. Add or subtract the objects.

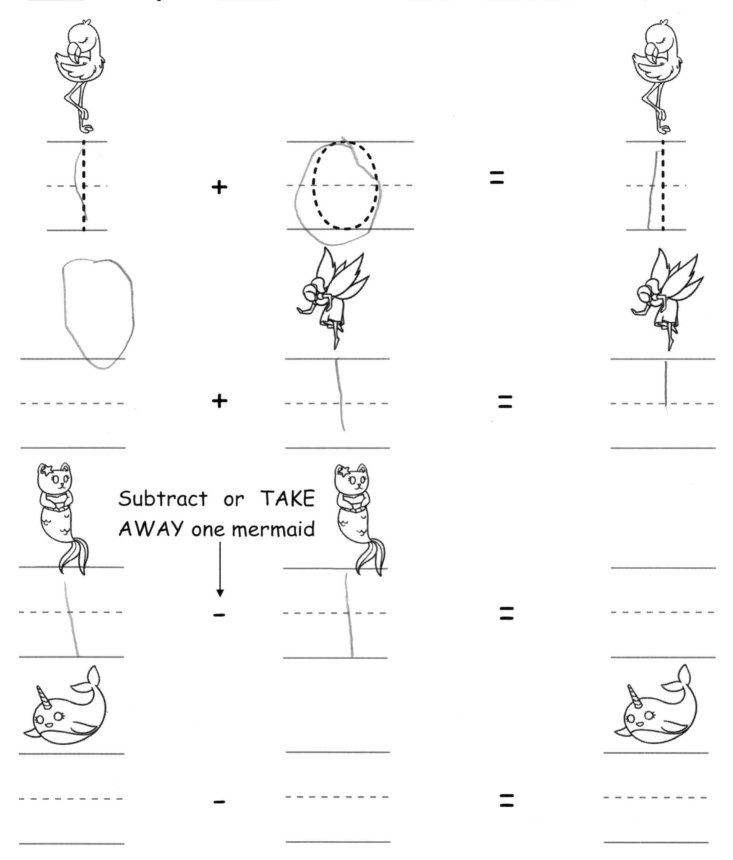

Subtract or TAKE AWAY one mermaid

Look at the picture carefully. Now turn the page.

One flower, one cloud, and one cupcake are missing. <u>Draw</u> and <u>color</u> a picture of the missing flower, the missing cloud, and the missing cupcake.

Say the number. Trace the number. Write the number.

I see 2 cats.

2 2 2 two two

2 2 2 2 2 2 2 2

2 2 2 2 2 2 2 2

Count the items. <u>Write</u> the number word in the puzzle. <u>Use</u> the Choice Box to help you.

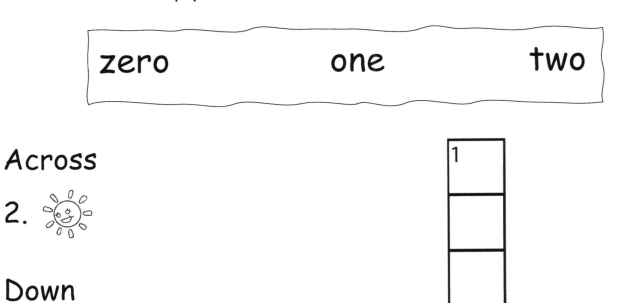

zero   one   two

Across

2.

Down

1.

Across

3.

Down

1.

2.

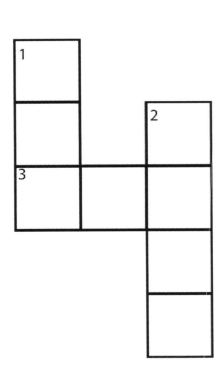

Count the objects. Write the number. Add the objects.

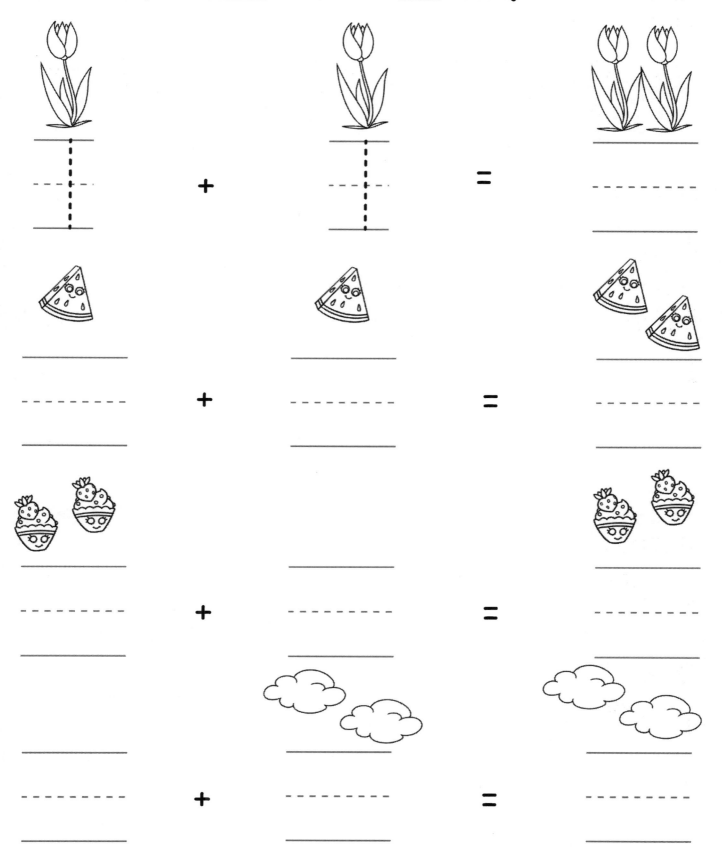

Count the objects. Write the number. Subtract or take away the objects.

- - - - - - - -   -   - - - - - - - -   =   - - - - - - - -
_____   _____   _____

- - - - - - - -   -   - - - - - - - -   =   - - - - - - - -
_____   _____   _____

- - - - - - - -   -   - - - - - - - -   =   - - - - - - - -
_____   _____   _____

- - - - - - - -   -   - - - - - - - -   =   - - - - - - - -
_____   _____   _____

Say the number. Trace the number. Write the number.

I see  fairies.

3 3 3 three three

3 3 3 3 3 3 3

3 3 3 3 3 3 3

Count the objects. Write the next number.

Count the objects. Write the number. Add the objects.

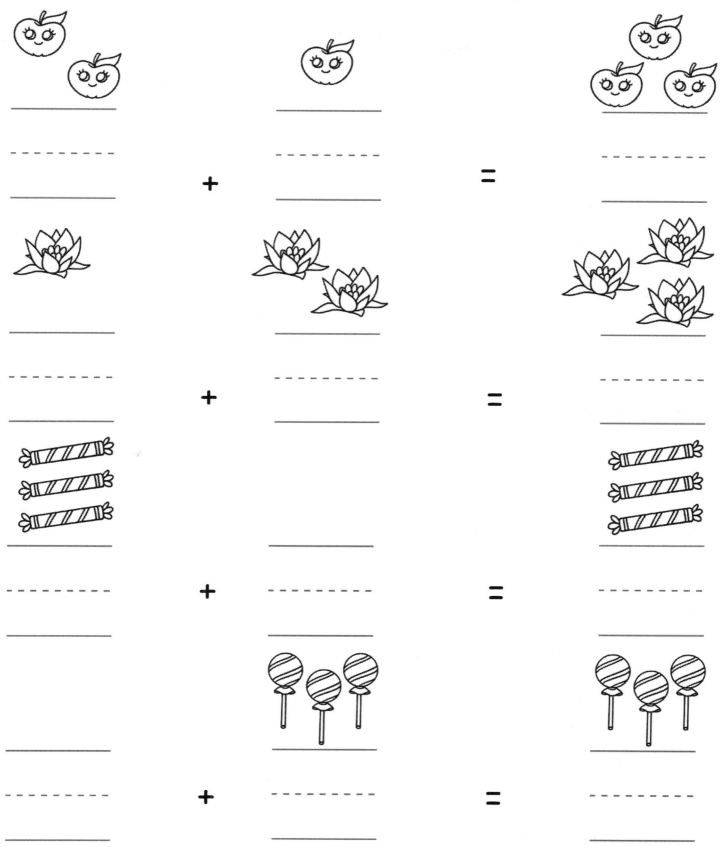

Count the objects. Write the number. Subtract the objects.

_____ - _____ = _____

_ _ _ _ _ _ _ _ _   -   _ _ _ _ _ _ _ _ _   =   _ _ _ _ _ _ _ _ _

_____   _____   _____

_____ - _____ = _____

_ _ _ _ _ _ _ _ _   -   _ _ _ _ _ _ _ _ _   =   _ _ _ _ _ _ _ _ _

_____   _____   _____

_____ - _____ = _____

_ _ _ _ _ _ _ _ _   -   _ _ _ _ _ _ _ _ _   =   _ _ _ _ _ _ _ _ _

_____   _____   _____

_____ - _____ = _____

_ _ _ _ _ _ _ _ _   -   _ _ _ _ _ _ _ _ _   =   _ _ _ _ _ _ _ _ _

_____   _____   _____

Say the number. Trace the number. Write the number.

I see 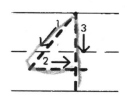 dogs.

444 four four four

4 4 4 4 4 4

4 4 4 4 4 4

Find the stars. Color them yellow.
Circle to show how many.

1   2   3   4

Find the heart. Color it red.
Circle to show how many.

1   2   3   4

Find the shapes. Color them green.
Circle to show how many.

1   2   3   4

Find the fairies. Color them pink.
Circle to show how many.

1   2   3   4

Count the objects. Write the number. Add the objects.

_____   _____   _____

- - - - - - -   **+**   - - - - - - -   **=**   - - - - - - -

_____   _____   _____

_____   _____   _____

- - - - - - -   **+**   - - - - - - -   **=**   - - - - - - -

_____   _____   _____

_____   _____   _____

- - - - - - -   **+**   - - - - - - -   **=**   - - - - - - -

_____   _____   _____

_____   _____   _____

- - - - - - -   **+**   - - - - - - -   **=**   - - - - - - -

_____   _____   _____

Count the objects. Write the number. Subtract the objects.

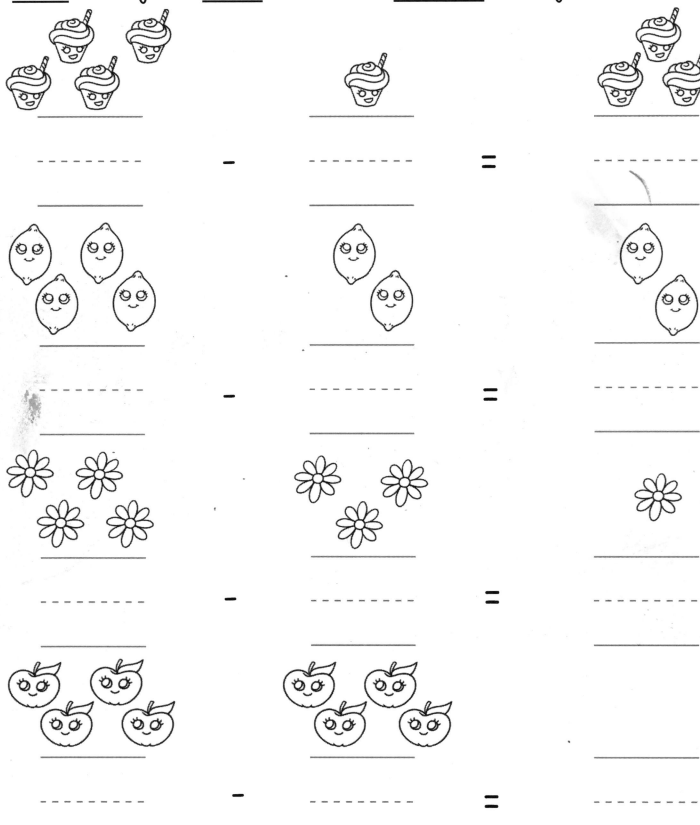

Say the number. Trace the number. Write the number.

I see 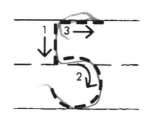 foxes.

5 5 5 five five

5 5 5 5 5 5 5

5 5 5 5 5 5 5

Count the objects. Write the number. Add the objects.

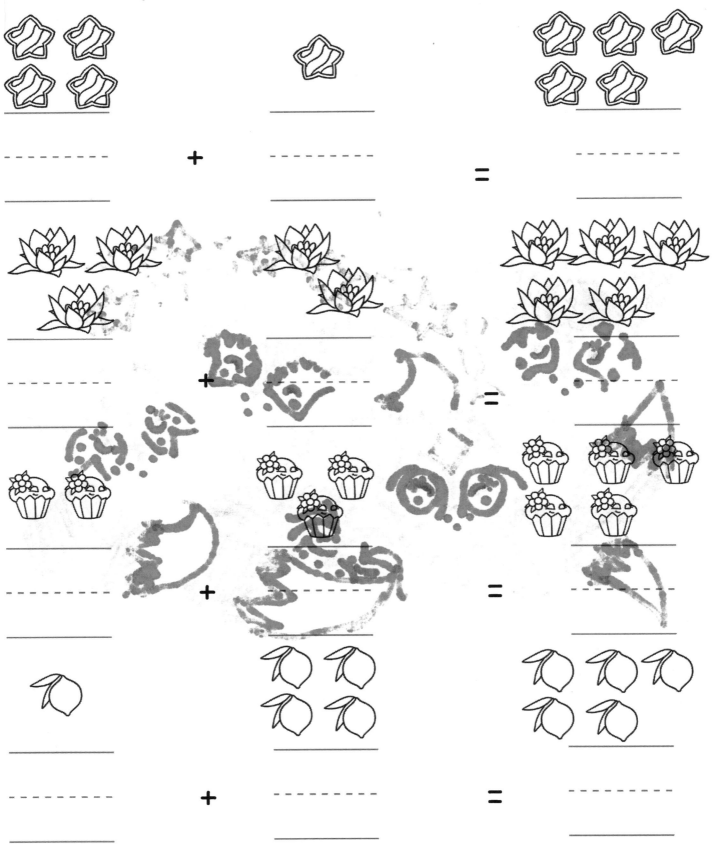

Count the objects. Write the number. Subtract the objects.

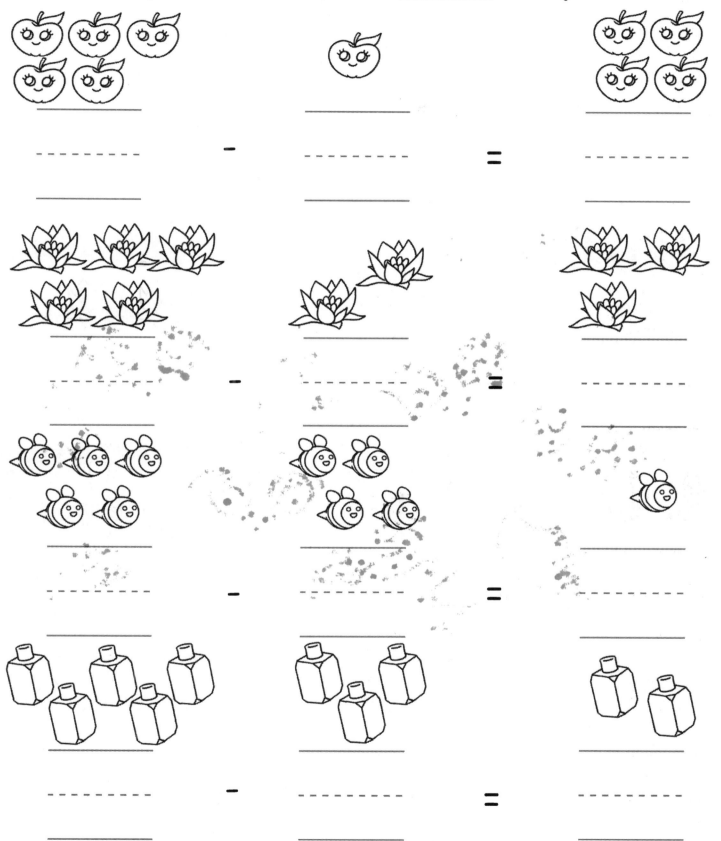

Find the mystery house.

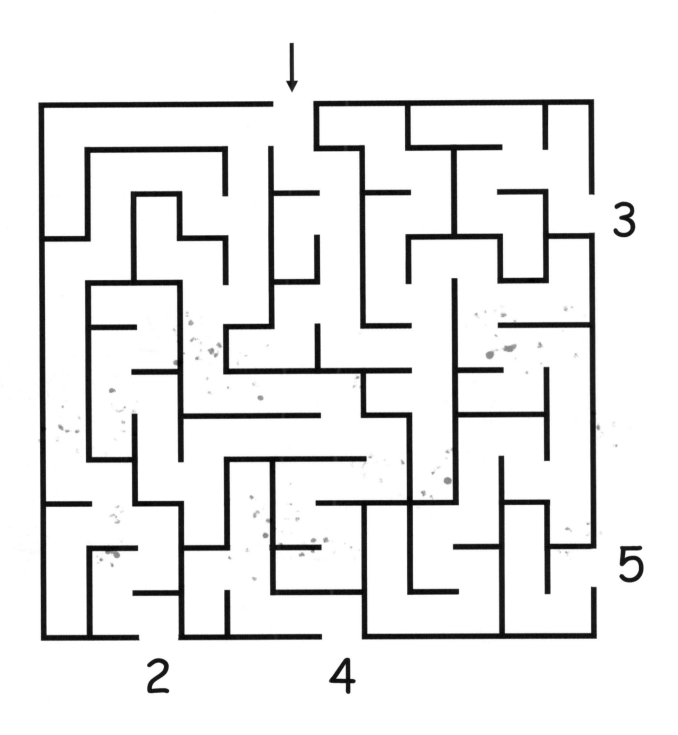

Circle the mystery house: 2   3   4   5

Say the number. Trace the number. Write the number.

I see  elves.

6 6 6 six six six

6 6 6 6 6 6 6

6 6 6 6 6 6 6

Count the items. Write the number word in the puzzle. Use the Choice Box to help you.

| zero | one | two | three |
| four | five | six | |

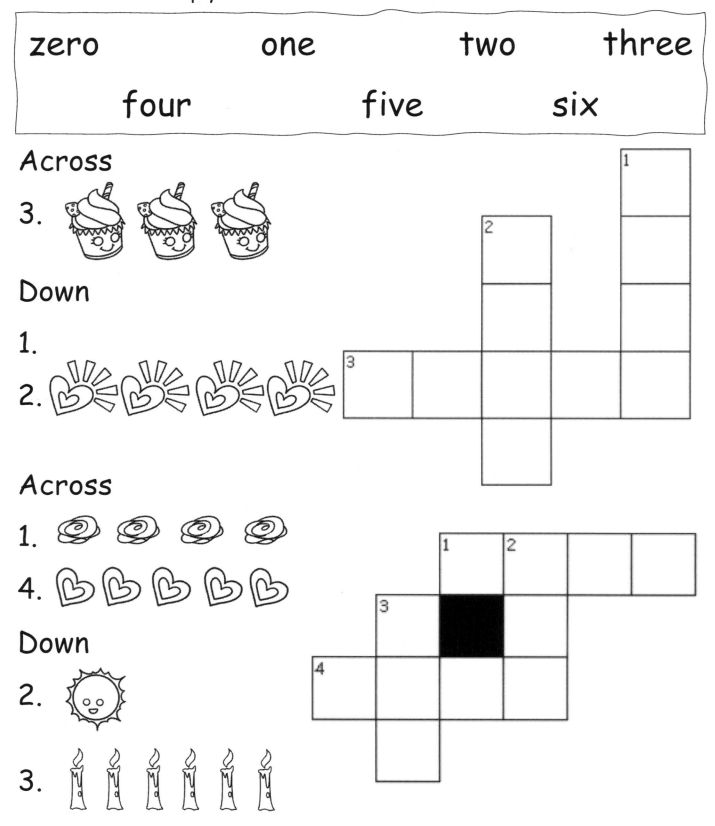

Across

3. 🧁🧁🧁

Down

1.

2. 💗💗💗💗

Across

1. 🌀🌀🌀🌀

4. 🤍🤍🤍🤍🤍

Down

2. ☀️

3. 🕯️🕯️🕯️🕯️🕯️🕯️

Count the objects. Write the number. Add the objects.

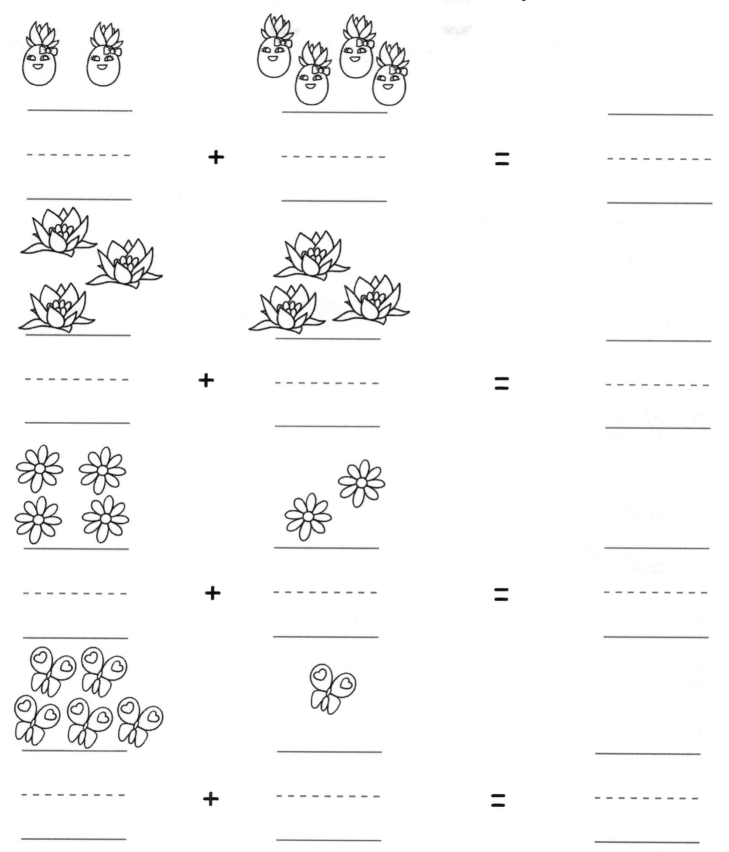

_____   +   _____   =   _____

_____   _____   _____

Count the objects. Write the number. Subtract the objects.

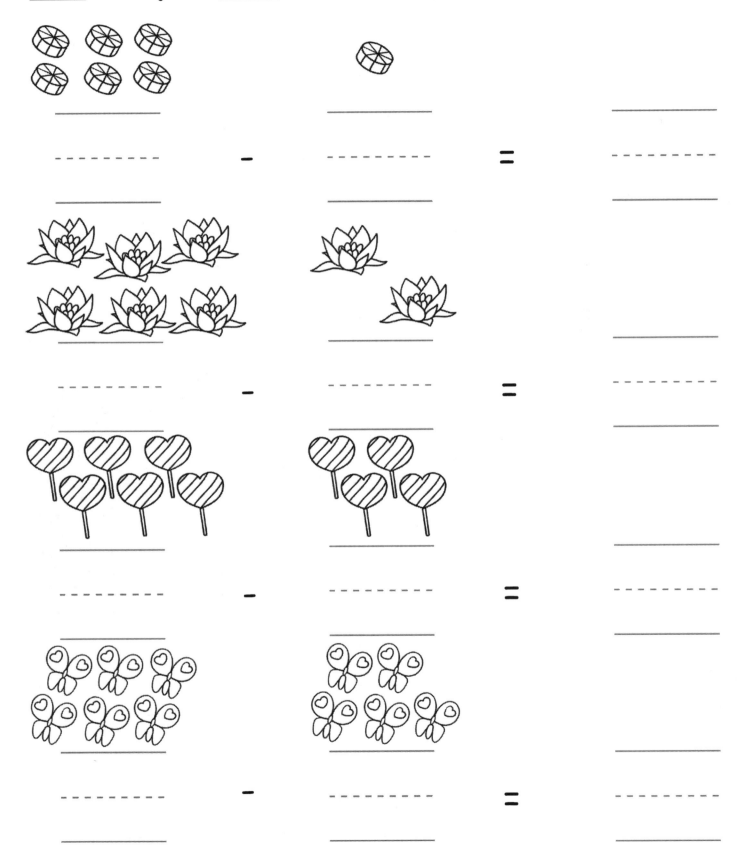

© 2020 Home Run Press, LLC

Say the number. Trace the number. Write the number.

I see   7   gnomes.

7 7 7 seven seven

Draw one more object. **Count** the objects. **Write** the number.

© 2020 Home Run Press, LLC

Count the objects. Write the number. Add the objects.

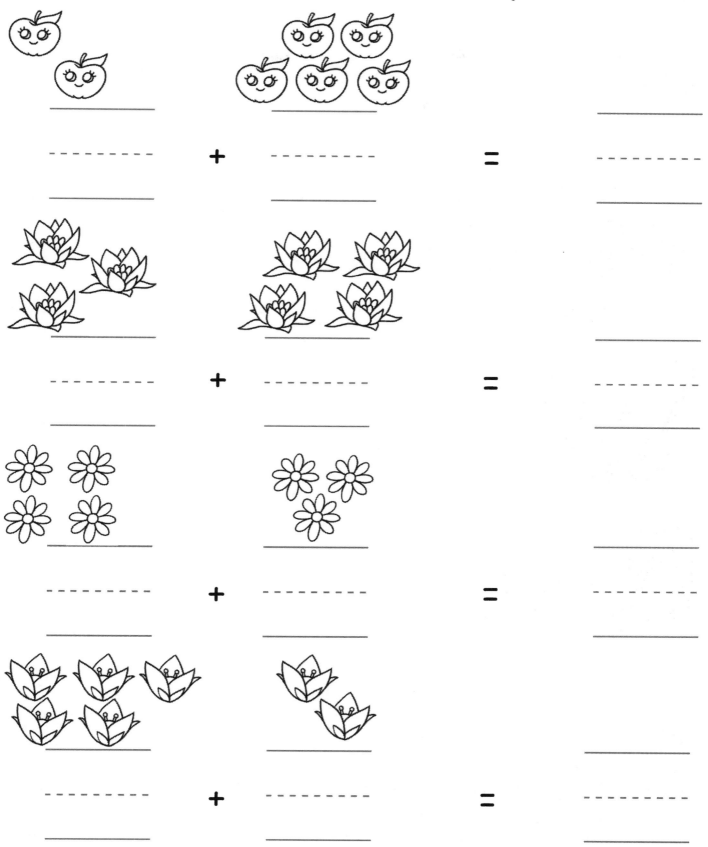

$+$ $=$

$+$ $=$

$+$ $=$

$+$ $=$

Count the objects. Write the number. Subtract the objects.

_____   _____   _____

- - - - - - - - -   **-**   - - - - - - - - -   **=**   - - - - - - - - -

_____   _____   _____

_____   _____   _____

- - - - - - - - -   **-**   - - - - - - - - -   **=**   - - - - - - - - -

_____   _____   _____

_____   _____   _____

- - - - - - - - -   **-**   - - - - - - - - -   **=**   - - - - - - - - -

_____   _____   _____

_____   _____   _____

- - - - - - - - -   **-**   - - - - - - - - -   **=**   - - - - - - - - -

_____   _____   _____

Count the objects. Write the number. Subtract the objects.

_____   _____   _____

- - - - - - - - -   **-**   - - - - - - - -   **=**   - - - - - - - -

_____   _____   _____

_____   _____   _____

- - - - - - - - -   **-**   - - - - - - - -   **=**   - - - - - - - -

_____   _____   _____

_____   _____   _____

- - - - - - - - -   **-**   - - - - - - - -   **=**   - - - - - - - -

_____   _____   _____

How many fruits are in the picture?

Circle your answer.   0   1   2   3   4   5   6   7

Count the objects. Draw a line to match the objects to the correct number.

© 2020 Home Run Press, LLC

Say the number. Trace the number. Write the number.

I see 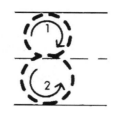 donuts.

Count the objects. Write the number. Add the objects.

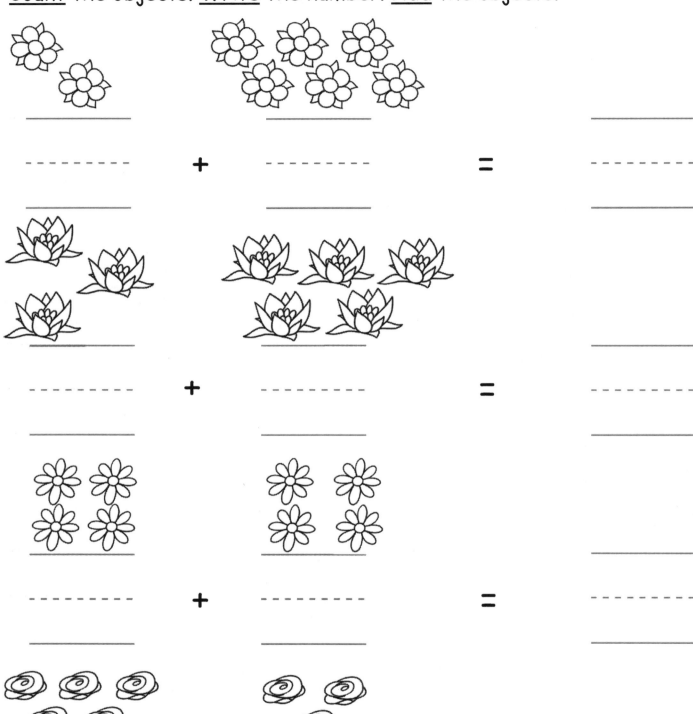

_____

_ _ _ _ _ _ _   **+**   _ _ _ _ _ _ _   **=**   _ _ _ _ _ _ _

_____   _____   _____

© 2020 Home Run Press, LLC

Count the objects. Write the number. Add the objects.

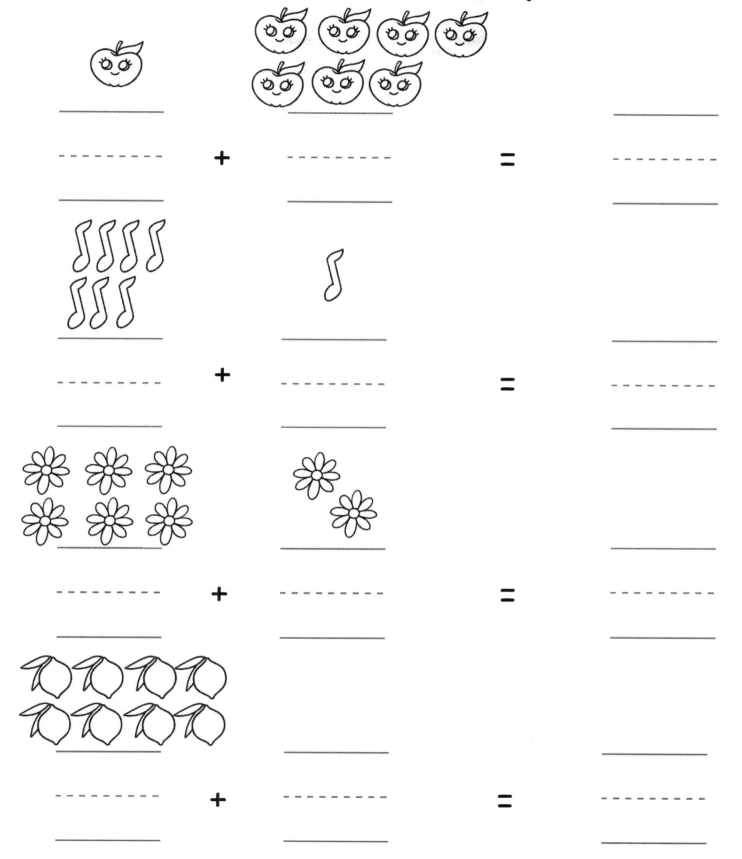

Count the objects. Write the number. Subtract the objects.

---------   **-**   ---------   **=**   ---------

---------   **-**   ---------   **=**   ---------

---------   **-**   ---------   **=**   ---------

---------   **-**   ---------   **=**   ---------

Count the objects. Write the number. Subtract the objects.

_____   _____   _____

- - - - - - - - -   −   - - - - - - - - -   =   - - - - - - - - -

_____   _____   _____

_____   _____   _____

- - - - - - - - -   −   - - - - - - - - -   =   - - - - - - - - -

_____   _____   _____

_____   _____   _____

- - - - - - - - -   −   - - - - - - - - -   =   - - - - - - - - -

_____   _____   _____

_____   _____   _____

- - - - - - - - -   −   - - - - - - - - -   =   - - - - - - - - -

_____   _____   _____

Count the number of each object. Circle the correct word. Trace it.

five   three

one   four

eight   two

five   three

four   six

seven   one

two   six

Color the cloud with the larger number in each pair.

Count the items. Write the number word in the puzzle. Use the Choice Box to help you.

zero	two	three	four
	five	eight	

Across

3.

5.

6.

Down

1.

2.

4.

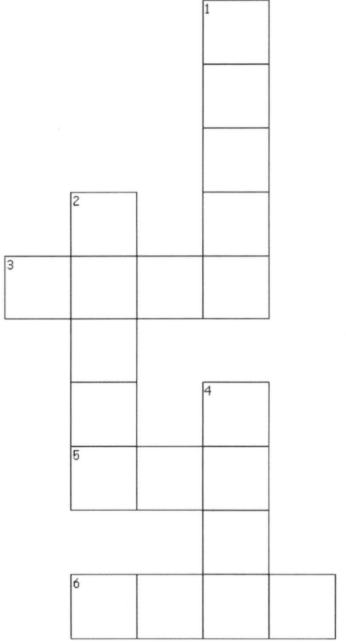

Say the number. Trace the number. Write the number.

I see **9** mermaids.

9 9 9 nine nine

a a a a a a a

a a a a a a a

Count the objects. Write the number. Add the objects.

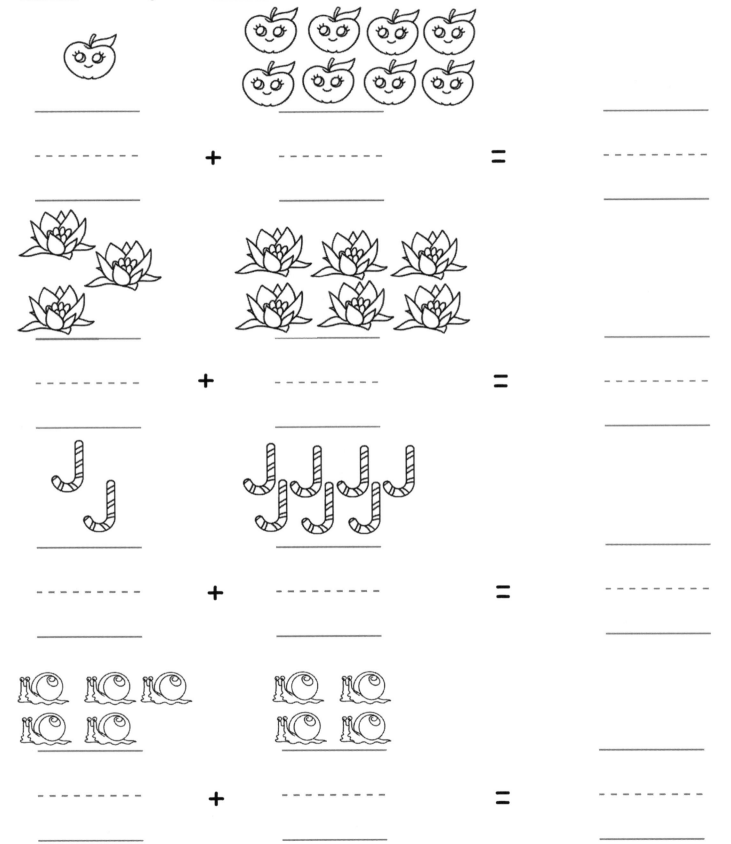

_____

\- - - - - - - - - **+** - - - - - - - - - **=** - - - - - - - - -

Count the objects. Write the number. Add the objects.

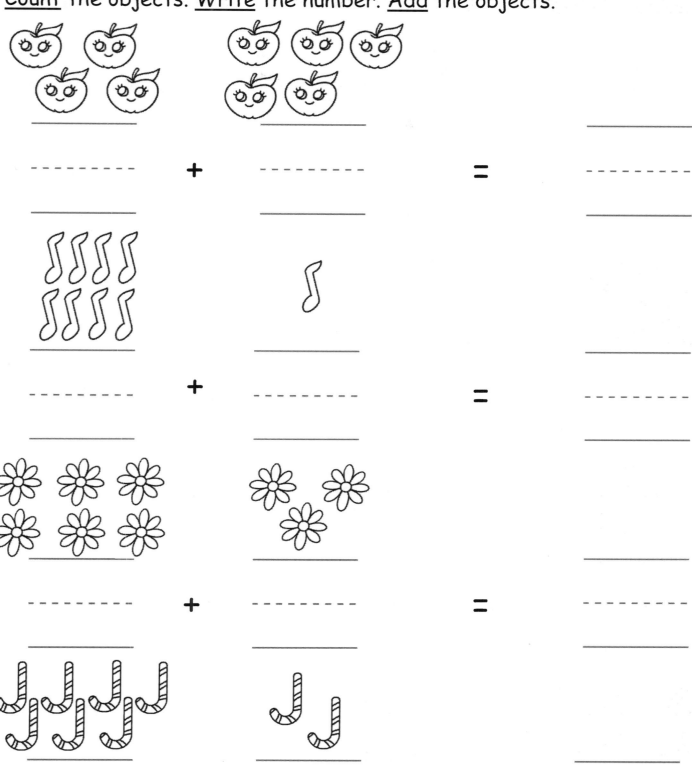

‒ ‒ ‒ ‒ ‒ ‒ ‒ ‒   +   ‒ ‒ ‒ ‒ ‒ ‒ ‒ ‒   =   ‒ ‒ ‒ ‒ ‒ ‒ ‒ ‒

‒ ‒ ‒ ‒ ‒ ‒ ‒ ‒   +   ‒ ‒ ‒ ‒ ‒ ‒ ‒ ‒   =   ‒ ‒ ‒ ‒ ‒ ‒ ‒ ‒

‒ ‒ ‒ ‒ ‒ ‒ ‒ ‒   +   ‒ ‒ ‒ ‒ ‒ ‒ ‒ ‒   =   ‒ ‒ ‒ ‒ ‒ ‒ ‒ ‒

‒ ‒ ‒ ‒ ‒ ‒ ‒ ‒   +   ‒ ‒ ‒ ‒ ‒ ‒ ‒ ‒   =   ‒ ‒ ‒ ‒ ‒ ‒ ‒ ‒

Count the objects. Write the number. Subtract the objects.

_____   _____   _____

- - - - - -   **-**   - - - - - -   **=**   - - - - - -

_____   _____   _____

- - - - - -   **-**   - - - - - -   **=**   - - - - - -

_____   _____   _____

- - - - - -   **-**   - - - - - -   **=**   - - - - - -

_____   _____   _____

- - - - - -   **-**   - - - - - -   **=**   - - - - - -

_____   _____   _____

Count the objects. Write the number. Subtract the objects.

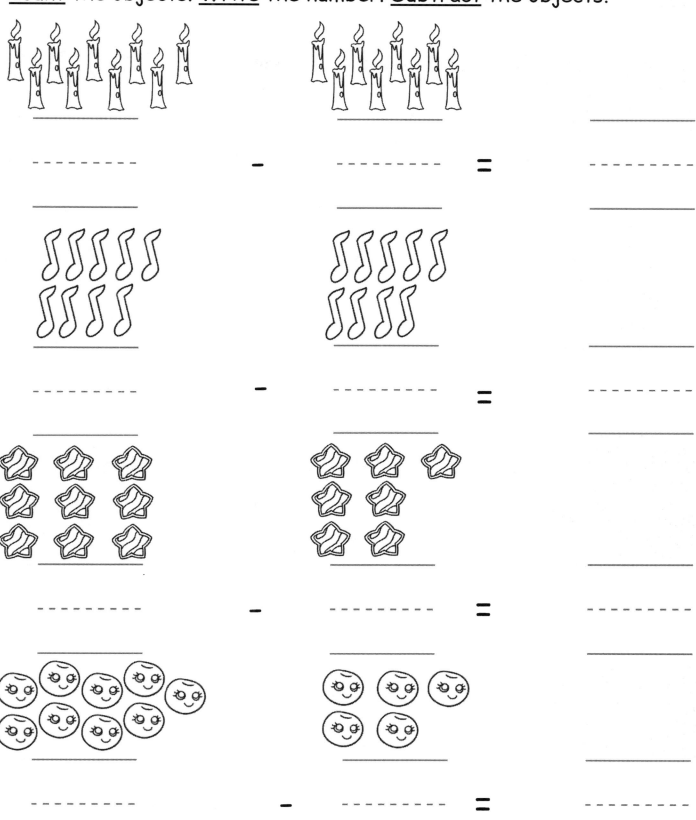

Color the cloud with the greatest number in each row.

Color the cloud with the least number in each row.

Find the clouds. Color them blue.
Circle to show how many.

2 3 4 5

Find the ladybugs. Color them red and black.
Circle to show how many.

1 2 3 4

Find the flowers. Color them yellow.
Circle to show how many.

6 7 8 9

Find the hearts on the microscope. Color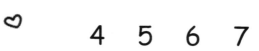
them pink. Circle to show how many.

4 5 6 7

Say the number. Trace the number. Write the number.

I see 10 houses.

10 10 10 ten ten

10 10 10 10 10

10 10 10 10 10

Count the objects. Write the number. Add the objects.

_ _ _ _ _ _ _   **+**   _ _ _ _ _ _ _   **=**   _ _ _ _ _ _ _

_ _ _ _ _ _ _   **+**   _ _ _ _ _ _ _   **=**   _ _ _ _ _ _ _

_ _ _ _ _ _ _   **+**   _ _ _ _ _ _ _   **=**   _ _ _ _ _ _ _

_ _ _ _ _ _ _   **+**   _ _ _ _ _ _ _   **=**   _ _ _ _ _ _ _

Count the objects. Write the number. Add the objects.

_____   _____   _____

- - - - - - - + - - - - - - - = - - - - - - -

_____   _____   _____

_____   _____   _____

- - - - - - - + - - - - - - - = - - - - - - -

_____   _____   _____

_____   _____   _____

- - - - - - - + - - - - - - - = - - - - - - -

_____   _____   _____

_____   _____   _____

- - - - - - - + - - - - - - - = - - - - - - -

_____   _____   _____

Count the objects. Write the number. Subtract the objects.

_____ - _____ = _____

_ _ _ _ _ _ _ _ _ _ _ _   -   _ _ _ _ _ _ _ _ _   =   _ _ _ _ _ _ _ _ _ _

_____ - _____ = _____

_ _ _ _ _ _ _ _ _ _ _ _   -   _ _ _ _ _ _ _ _ _   =   _ _ _ _ _ _ _ _ _ _

_____ - _____ = _____

_ _ _ _ _ _ _ _ _ _ _ _   -   _ _ _ _ _ _ _ _ _   =   _ _ _ _ _ _ _ _ _ _

_____ - _____ = _____

_ _ _ _ _ _ _ _ _ _ _ _   -   _ _ _ _ _ _ _ _ _   =   _ _ _ _ _ _ _ _ _ _

_____ - _____ = _____

Count the objects. Write the number. Subtract the objects.

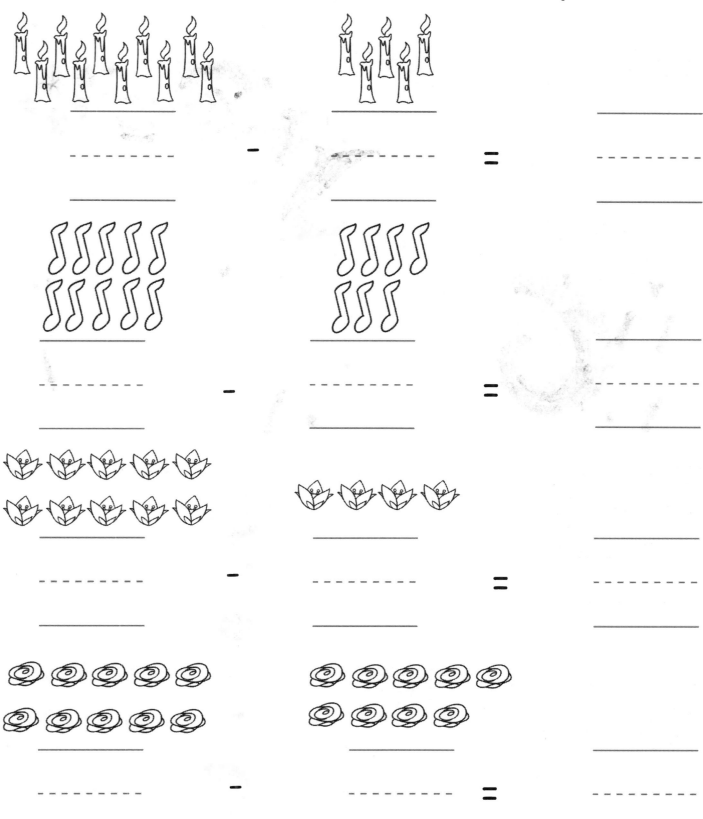

Find the sun. Color it yellow.

Circle to show how many.

(1) 2   3   4

Find the bees. Color them yellow and black.

Circle to show how many.

 1   2 (3) 4

Find the flowers. Color them yellow.

Circle to show how many.

 7   8   9 (10)

Find the sunflowers. Color them yellow.

Circle to show how many.

 1   2 (3) 4

Say the number. Trace the number. Write the number.

I see 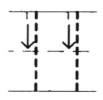 pineapples.

11 11 11 eleven eleven

Count the items. Write the number word in the puzzle. Use the Choice Box to help you.

nine	five	eleven	six
three	eight	ten	seven

Down

1. [three suns]

2. [five parachutes]

3. [seven items]

4. [six hearts]

7. [nine items]

Across

5. [eleven items]

6. [eight items]

8. [ten candles]

Color 1 snail.

How many snails are NOT colored?

Circle your answer. 1 2 3 4 5 6 7 8 9 10

How many snails are there in all?

Circle your answer. 10 11 12 13 14 15 16 17 18 19

Color 10 flowers.

How many flowers are NOT colored?

Circle your answer. 1 2 3 4 5 6 7 8 9

How many flowers are there in all?

Circle your answer. 10 11 12 13 14 15 16 17 18 19

2 plus what number equals 3?

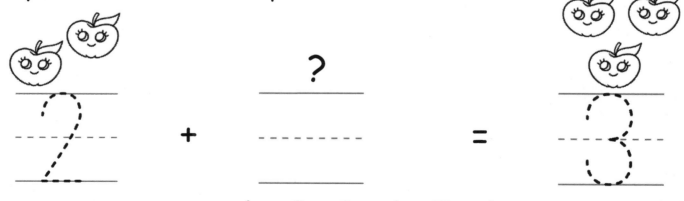

Circle your answer. 1 2 3 4 5 6 7 8 9 10

Count the objects. Write the number. Add and subtract the objects.

_____ _____ _____

- - - - - - - - - - + - - - - - - - - - - = - - - - - - - - - -

_____ _____ _____

_____ _____ _____

- - - - - - - - - - − - - - - - - - - - - = - - - - - - - - - -

_____ _____ _____

1 plus what number equals 4?

 ?

1 + ____ = 4

Circle your answer.   0   1   2   3   4   5

Say the number. Trace the number. Write the number.

I see **12** flamingos.

12 12 12 twelve

12 12 12 12 12

12 12 12 12 12

Circle the lightest.

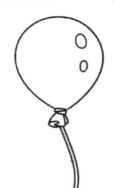 a balloon

 a flamingo

Cross out the heaviest.

 a balloon

 a flamingo

Circle the longest.

 a tulip

 a sunflower

Cross out the shortest.

 a tulip

 a sunflower

Color 10 bananas.

How many bananas are NOT colored?

Circle your answer.　　　　　1　　2　　3　　4　　5　　6

How many bananas are there in all?

Circle your answer.　10　11　12　13　14　15　16　17　18　19

Color 2 flowers.

How many flowers are NOT colored?

Circle your answer.　1　　2　　3　　4　　5　　6　　7　　8　　9　　10

How many flowers are there in all?

Circle your answer.　10　11　12　13　14　15　16　17　18　19

3 plus what number equals 6?

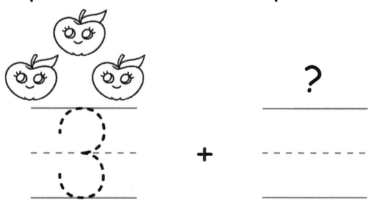
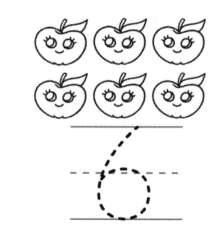

3 + _____ = 6

Circle your answer.　1　　2　　3　　4　　5　　6　　7　　8　　9　10

Count the objects. Write the number. Add and subtract the objects.

_____   _____   _____

- - - - - - - -   +   - - - - - - - -   =   - - - - - - - -

_____   _____   _____

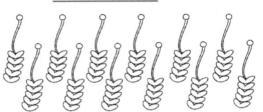

_____   _____   _____

- - - - - - - -   -   - - - - - - - -   =   - - - - - - - -

_____   _____   _____

5 plus what number equals 7?

   ?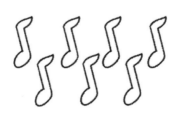

   +   =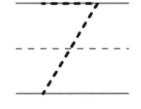

Circle your answer.   0   1   2   3   4   5

Say the number. Trace the number. Write the number.

I see **13** whales.

13 13 13 thirteen

13 13 13 13 13

13 13 13 13 13

My friends have a ton of stuffed animals. <u>Make</u> a chart of all our stuffed anilams below. Liam's chart is done for you.

0 1 2 3 4 5 6 7 8 9 10 11 12 13

Color 10 flowers.

How many flowers are NOT colored?

Circle your answer.　　2　3　4　5　6　7　8

How many flowers are there in all?

Circle your answer.　10　11　12　13　14　15　16　17　18　19

Color 3 bottles.

How many bottles are NOT colored?

Circle your answer.　1　2　3　4　5　6　7　8　9　10

How many bottles are there in all?

Circle your answer.　10　11　12　13　14　15　16　17　18　19

4 plus what number equals 6?

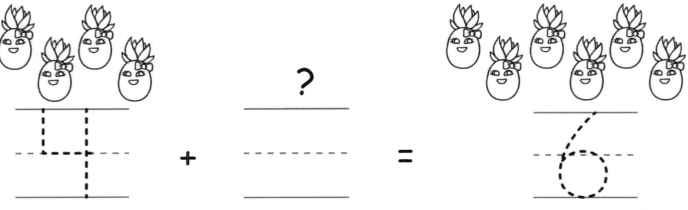

Circle your answer.　1　2　3　4　5　6　7　8　9　10

Count the objects. Write the number. Add and subtract the objects.

_____   _____   _____

- - - - - - - - -   +   - - - - - - - - -   =   - - - - - - - - -

_____   _____   _____

_____   _____   _____

- - - - - - - - -   -   - - - - - - - - -   =   - - - - - - - - -

_____   _____   _____

5 plus what number equals 8?

_____   _____

- - - - - 5 - - - -   +   - - - - - - - - -   =   - - - - 8 - - - -

_____   _____

Circle your answer.   0   1   2   3   4   5

Say the number. Trace the number. Write the number.

I see   14   butterflies.

14   14   fourteen

14   14   14   14   14

14   14   14   14

My Grandma baked 2 apple pies. I ate a half of the pies. How many pies are left?

Circle your answer:

0   1   2   3   4   5

I found 6 shells. My brother broke a half of the shells. How many shells are left?

Circle your answer:

0   1   2   3   4   5

I got 4 cupcakes. I ate a half of them. How many cupcakes are left?

Circle your answer:

0   1   2   3   4   5

My birthday cake weighed 8 pounds! My friends ate a half of the cake. How many pounds are left?

Circle your answer: 0   1   2   3   4   5

Color ☐10 flowers.

How many flowers are NOT colored?

Circle your answer.　　2　3　4　5　6　7　8

How many flowers are there in all?

Circle your answer.　10　11　12　13　14　15　16　17　18　19

Color ☐4 cupcakes.

How many cupcakes are NOT colored?

Circle your answer.　1　2　3　4　5　6　7　8　9　10

How many cupcakes are there in all?

Circle your answer.　10　11　12　13　14　15　16　17　18　19

2 plus what number equals 7?

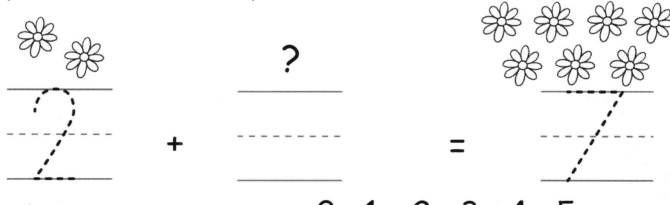

Circle your answer.　　　0　1　2　3　4　5

Count the objects. Write the number. Add and subtract the objects.

_____   _ _ _ _ _ _ _   _ _ _ _ _ _ _

_ _ _ _ _ _ _ _   **+**   _ _ _ _ _ _ _   **=**   _ _ _ _ _ _ _

_____   _____

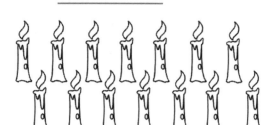   

_____   _____   _____

_ _ _ _ _ _ _ _   **-**   _ _ _ _ _ _ _   **=**   _ _ _ _ _ _ _

_____   _____   _____

4 plus what number equals 8?

   ?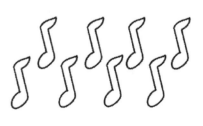

4   **+**   _ _ _ _ _   **=**   8

Circle your answer.   0   1   2   3   4   5

76   © 2020 Home Run Press, LLC

Say the number. Trace the number. Write the number.

I see **15** fruits.

15 15 15 15 fifteen

15 15 15 15 15

15 15 15 15 15

Count the items. Write the number word in the puzzle. Use the Choice Box to help you.

twelve	fifteen	eleven	ten
thirteen	eight	fourteen	

Down

2.

3.

4.

5.

Across

1.

6.

7.

Color 5 lemons.

How many lemons are NOT colored?

Circle your answer. 1 2 3 4 5 6 7 8 9 10

How many lemons are there in all?

Circle your answer. 10 11 12 13 14 15 16 17 18 19

Color 10 candies.

How many candies are NOT colored?

Circle your answer. 1 2 3 4 5 6 7 8 9 10

How many candies are there in all?

Circle your answer. 10 11 12 13 14 15 16 17 18 19

4 plus what number equals 9?

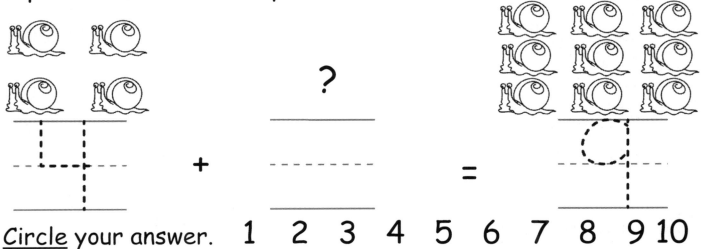

4 + _____ = 9

Circle your answer. 1 2 3 4 5 6 7 8 9 10

Count the objects. Write the number. Add and subtract the objects.

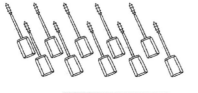

_____   +   _____   =   _____

- - - - - - -   - - - - - - -   - - - - - - -

_____   _____   _____

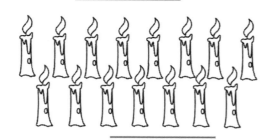   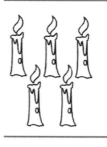

- - - - - - -   -   - - - - - - -   =   - - - - - - -

_____   _____   _____

6 plus what number equals 9?

   ?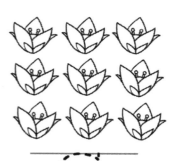

_____   _____   _____

6   +   - - - - - - -   =   9

_____   _____   _____

Circle your answer.   0   1   2   3   4   5

Say the number. Trace the number. Write the number.

I see 16 cherries.

16 16 16 sixteen

16 16 16 16 16

16 16 16 16 16

Color 6 strawberries.

How many strawberries are NOT colored?

Circle your answer.   1 2   3   4   5   6   7   8   9   10

How many strawberries are there in all?

Circle your answer.   10 11 12 13 14 15 16 17 18 19

Color 10 candies.

How many candies are NOT colored?

Circle your answer.   1 2   3   4   5   6   7   8   9   10

How many candies are there in all?

Circle your answer.   10 11 12 13 14 15 16 17 18 19

5 plus what number equals 7?

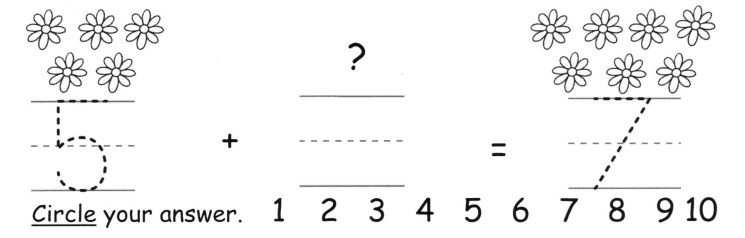

Circle your answer.   1   2   3   4   5   6   7   8   9 10

I am a number that is smaller than 5 and bigger than 3. <u>What number</u> am I?

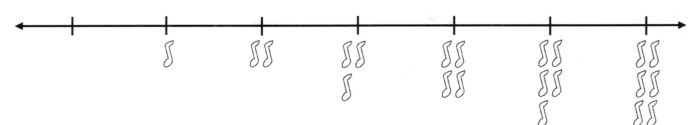

<u>Circle</u> your answer.   0 1 2 3 4 5 6 7

I am a number that is smaller than 11 and bigger than 9. <u>What number</u> am I?

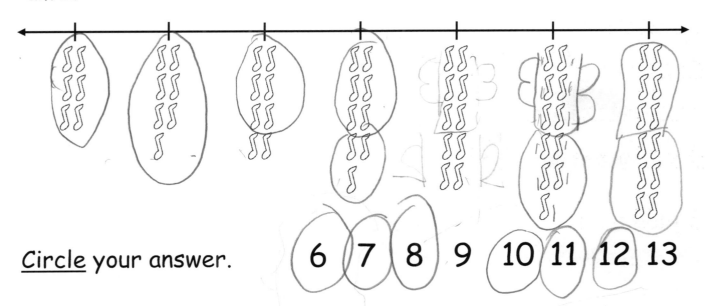

<u>Circle</u> your answer.   6 7 8 9 10 11 12 13

I am a number that is smaller than 15 and bigger than 13. <u>What number</u> am I?

<u>Circle</u> your answer.   9 10 11 12 13 14 15 16

Count the objects. Write the number. Add and subtract the objects.

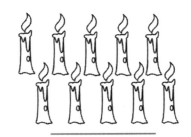

_____

_____

\- - - - - - - - -   +   \- - - - - - - - -   =   \- - - - - - - - -

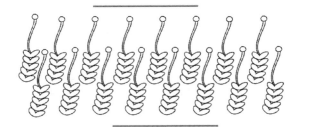

_____

_____

\- - - - - - - - -   -   \- - - - - - - - -   =   \- - - - - - - - -

1 plus what number equals 8?

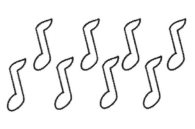

\- - - - -   +   \- - - - -   =   \- - 8 - -

Circle your answer.   0   1   2   3   4   5   6   7   8

Say the number. Trace the number. Write the number.

I see 17 cupcakes.

17 17 seventeen

How many butterflies are there?

Circle your answer.　　5　6　7　8　9　10　11　12

Color each heart red. How many hearts are there?

Circle your answer.　　8　9　10　11　12　13　14　15

Color each bigger wing yellow. How many bigger wings are there?

Circle your answer.　　8　9　10　11　12　13　14　15

2 plus what number equals 8?

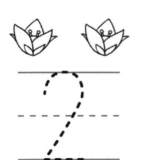　?　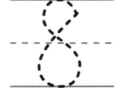

2　+　＿＿＿　=　8

Circle your answer.　1　2　3　4　5　6　7　8　9　10

Color 7 cherries.

How many cherries are NOT colored?

Circle your answer.   1 2   3   4   5   6   7   8   9   10

How many cherries are there in all?

Circle your answer.   10 11 12 13 14 15 16 17 18 19

Color 10 flowers.

How many flowers are NOT colored?

Circle your answer.   1 2   3   4   5   6   7   8   9   10

How many flowers are there in all?

Circle your answer.   10 11 12 13 14 15 16 17 18 19

10 plus what number equals 14?

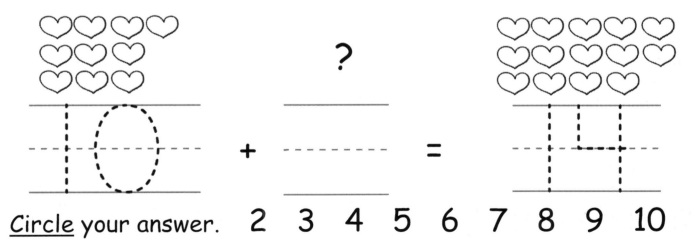

Circle your answer.   2   3   4   5   6   7   8   9   10

Count the objects. Write the number. Add and subtract the objects.

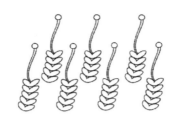

_____   +   _____   =   _____

_ _ _ _ _ _ _ _ _ _   _ _ _ _ _ _ _ _ _ _   _ _ _ _ _ _ _ _ _ _

_____   _____   _____

_____   -   _____   =   _____

_ _ _ _ _ _ _ _ _ _   _ _ _ _ _ _ _ _ _ _   _ _ _ _ _ _ _ _ _ _

_____   _____   _____

4 plus what number equals 9?

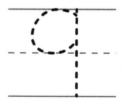

4   +   _____   =   9

_ _ _ _ _ _ _ _ _ _

Circle your answer.   0   1   2   3   4   5   6   7

Say the number. Trace the number. Write the number.

I see 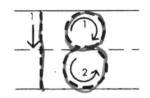 flowers.

18 18 18 eighteen

18 18 18 18 18

18 18 18 18 18

I am a number that is smaller than 8 and bigger than 6. What number am I?

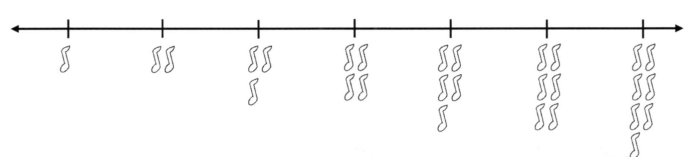

Circle your answer.   0   1   2   3   4   5   6   7

I am a number that is smaller than 15 and bigger than 13. What number am I?

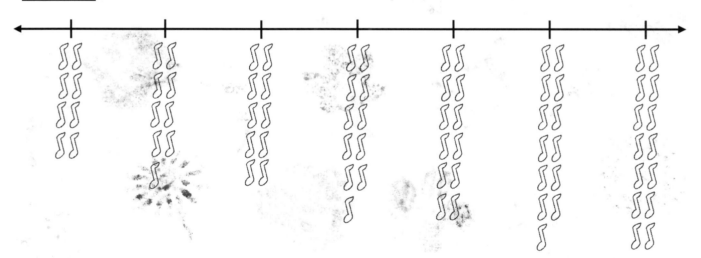

Circle your answer.   8   9   10   11   12   13   14   15

I am a number that is smaller than 18 and bigger than 16. What number am I?

Circle your answer.   12   13   14   15   16   17   18   19

Color 8 cherries.

How many cherries are NOT colored?

Circle your answer.   1 2   3   4   5   6   7   8   9   10

How many cherries are there in all?

Circle your answer.   10 11 12 13 14 15 16 17 18 19

Color 10 candies.

How many candies are NOT colored?

Circle your answer.   1 2   3   4   5   6   7   8   9   10

How many candies are there in all?

Circle your answer.   10 11 12 13 14 15 16 17 18 19

3 plus what number equals 7?

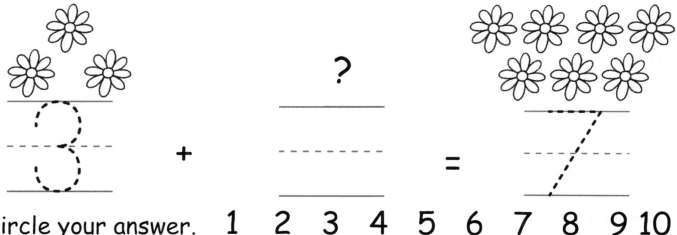

Circle your answer.   1   2   3   4   5   6   7   8   9 10

Count the objects. Write the number. Add and subtract the objects.

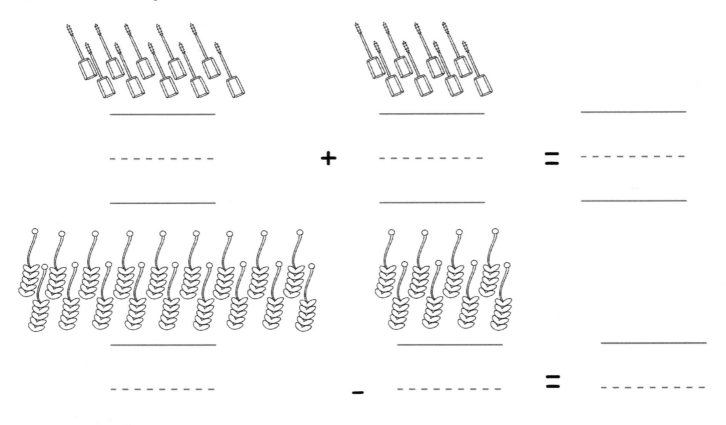

_____   +   _____   =   _____

_____   -   _____   =   _____

10 plus what number equals 12?

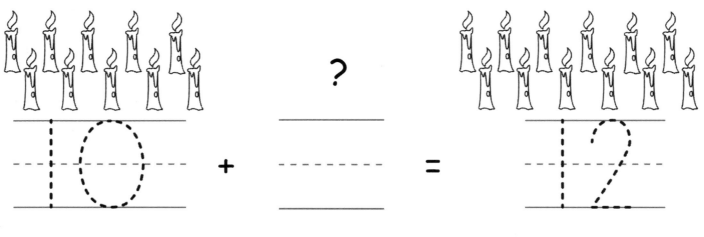

Circle your answer.   1   2   3   4   5   6   7   8   9 10

Say the number. Trace the number. Write the number.

I see $\quad$ **19** $\quad$ crayons.

19 $\quad$ 19 $\quad$ nineteen

19 19 19 19 19

19 19 19 19 19

Color each star yellow. <u>How many stars</u> are there?

Circle your answer.   5   6   7   8   9   10   11   12

Color each ball red. <u>How many balls</u> are there?

Circle your answer.   8   9   10   11   12   13   14   15

Color each cloud blue. <u>How many clouds</u> are there?

Circle your answer.   1   2   3   4   5   6   7   8

Color 9 candies.

How many candies are NOT colored?

Circle your answer.   1 2   3   4   5   6   7   8   9   10

How many candies are there in all?

Circle your answer.   11   12   13   14   15   16   17   18   19

Color 10 cherries.

How many cherries are NOT colored?

Circle your answer.   1 2   3   4   5   6   7   8   9   10

How many cherries are there in all?

Circle your answer.   11   12   13   14   15   16   17   18   19

10 plus what number equals 18?

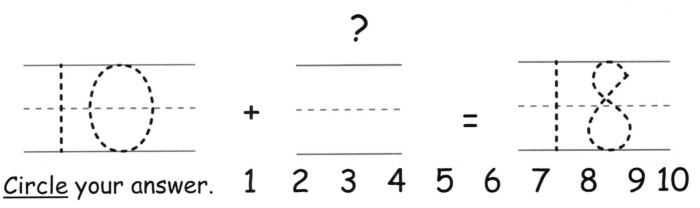

Circle your answer.   1   2   3   4   5   6   7   8   9 10

Count the objects. Write the number. Add and subtract the objects.

_____   _____   _____

- - - - - - - -   +   - - - - - - - -   =   - - - - - - - -

_____   _____   _____

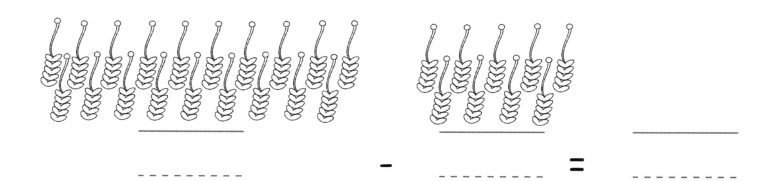

_____   _____   _____

- - - - - - - -   -   - - - - - - - -   =   - - - - - - - -

_____   _____   _____

10 plus what number equals 13?

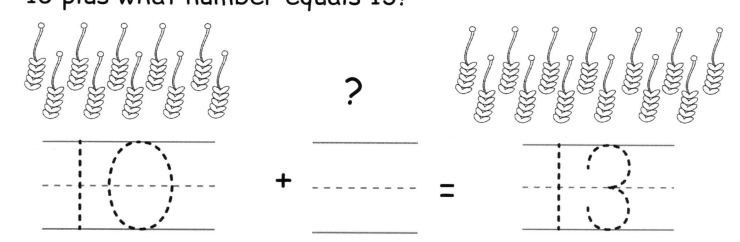

Circle your answer.   1   2   3   4   5   6   7   8   9 10

Say the number. Trace the number. Write the number.

I see **20** candies.

20 20 twenty

20 20 20 20

20 20 20 20

Color 10 cherries.

How many cherries are NOT colored?

Circle your answer.   1 2   3   4   5   6   7   8   9   10

How many cherries are there in all?

Circle your answer.   12 13 14 15 16 17 18 19 20

Color 10 candies.

How many candies are NOT colored?

Circle your answer.   1 2   3   4   5   6   7   8   9   10

How many candies are there in all?

Circle your answer.   12 13 14 15 16 17 18 19 20

10 plus what number equals 11?

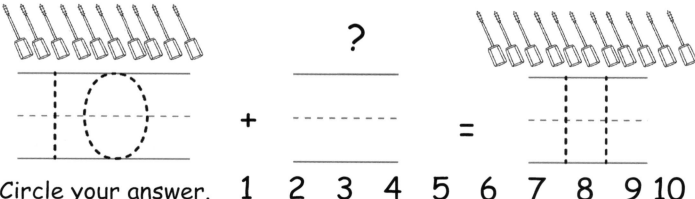

Circle your answer.   1   2   3   4   5   6   7   8   9 10

10 plus what number equals 15?

 ?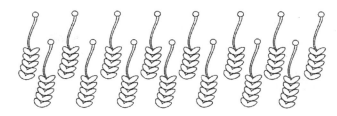

10 + ___ = 15

Circle your answer.   2 3 4 5 6 7 8 9 10

10 plus what number equals 17?

 ?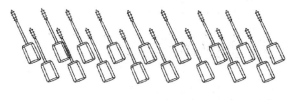

10 + ___ = 17

Circle your answer.   2 3 4 5 6 7 8 9 10

How many legs do 3 squirrels have altogether?

Circle your answer.   1 2 3 4 5 6 7 8 9

Count the objects. Write the number. Add and subtract the objects.

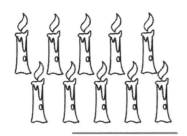
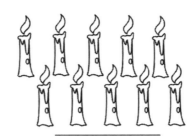

------------- + ------------- = -------------

------------- - ------------- = -------------

10 plus what number equals 16?

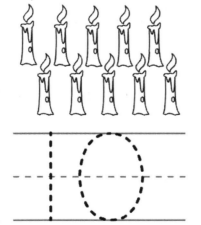

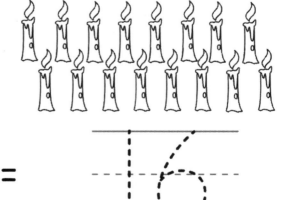

10 + _____ = 16

Circle your answer. 1 2 3 4 5 6 7 8 9 10

10 plus what number equals 19?

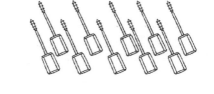 ?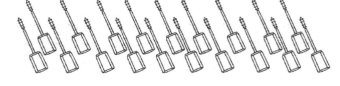

10 + _____ = 19

Circle your answer.　1　2　3　4　5　6　7　8　9　10

10 plus what number equals 20?

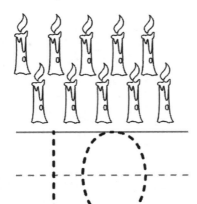 ?

10 + _____ = 20

Circle your answer.　1　2　3　4　5　6　7　8　9　10

How many groups of 5 can be made out of 10 cupcakes?

Circle your answer.　　1　2　3　4　5　6　7　8

Answer Key

Page 8
1

Page 10
$0 + 1 = 1$

$1 - 1 = 0$

$1 - 0 = 1$

Page 14
Across

2. one

Down

1. zero

Across

3. one

Down

1. two

2. zero

Page 15
$1 + 1 = 2$

$1 + 1 = 2$

$2 + 0 = 2$

$0 + 2 = 2$

Page 16
$2 - 1 = 1$

$2 - 1 = 1$

$2 - 0 = 2$

$1 - 1 = 0$

Page 18
3

2

1

3

Page 19
$2 + 1 = 3$

$1 + 2 = 3$

$3 + 0 = 3$

$0 + 3 = 3$

Page 21
$3 - 1 = 2$

$3 - 2 = 1$

$3 - 3 = 0$

$3 - 0 = 3$

Page 22
2

1

3

3

Page 23
$3 + 1 = 4$

$2 + 2 = 4$

$1 + 3 = 4$

$0 + 4 = 4$

Page 24
$4 - 1 = 3$

$4 - 2 = 2$

$4 - 3 = 1$

$4 - 4 = 0$

Page 26
$4 + 1 = 5$

$3 + 2 = 5$

$2 + 3 = 5$

$1 + 4 = 5$

Page 27
$5 - 1 = 4$

$5 - 2 = 3$

$5 - 4 = 1$

$5 - 3 = 2$

Page 28
2

Page 30
Across

3. three

Down

1. zero

2. four

Page 30
Across

1. four

4. five

Down

2. one

3. six

Page 31
$2 + 4 = 6$

$3 + 3 = 6$

$4 + 2 = 6$

$5 + 1 = 6$

Page 32
$6 - 1 = 5$

$6 - 2 = 4$

$6 - 4 = 2$

$6 - 5 = 1$

Page 34
3

5

4

2

6

Page 35
$2 + 5 = 7$

$3 + 4 = 7$

$4 + 3 = 7$

$5 + 2 = 7$

Page 36
$7 - 1 = 6$

$7 - 2 = 5$

$7 - 3 = 4$

$7 - 4 = 3$

Page 37
$7 - 5 = 2$

$7 - 6 = 1$

$7 - 7 = 0$

7

Page 40
$2 + 6 = 8$

$3 + 5 = 8$

$4 + 4 = 8$

$5 + 3 = 8$

Page 41
$1 + 7 = 8$

$7 + 1 = 8$

$6 + 2 = 8$

$8 + 0 = 8$

Answer Key

Page 42

8 − 1 = 7

8 − 3 = 5

8 − 4 = 4

8 − 2 = 6

Page 43

8 − 5 = 3

8 − 6 = 2

8 − 7 = 1

8 − 8 = 0

Page 44

five

four

eight

three

four

one

six

Page 45

8

3

8

6

7

Page 46

Across

3. five

5. two

6. zero

Down

1. three

2. eight

4. four

Page 48

1 + 8 = 9

3 + 6 = 9

2 + 7 = 9

5 + 4 = 9

Page 49

4 + 5 = 9

8 + 1 = 9

6 + 3 = 9

7 + 2 = 9

Page 50

9 − 1 = 8

9 − 3 = 6

9 − 4 = 5

9 − 2 = 7

Page 51

9 − 8 = 1

9 − 9 = 0

9 − 7 = 2

9 − 5 = 4

Page 52

8

8

9

7

8

Page 53

2

3

0

2

3

Page 54

5

2

8

5

Page 56

4 + 6 = 10

3 + 7 = 0

2 + 8 = 10

5 + 5 = 10

Page 57

1 + 9 = 10

8 + 2 = 0

6 + 4 = 10

7 + 3 = 10

Page 58

10 − 1 = 9

10 − 3 = 7

10 − 6 = 4

10 − 2 = 8

Page 59

10 − 5 = 5

10 − 7 = 3

10 − 4 = 6

10 − 9 = 1

Page 60

1

3

10

3

Page 62

Across

5. eleven

6. eight

8. nine

Down

1. three

2. five

3. seven

4. six

7. ten

Page 63

10

11

1

11

3

Page 64

10 + 1 = 11

11 − 1 = 10

3

Page 66

a balloon

a flamingo

a sunflower

a tulip

Page 67

2

12

10

12

3

Answer Key

Page 68

10 + 2 = 12

12 - 2 = 10

2

Page 70

Alex 10

Michael 13

Emma 12

Liam 11

Page 71

3

13

10

13

2

Page 72

10 + 3 = 13

13 - 3 = 10

3

Page 74

1

3

2

4

Page 75

4

14

10

14

5

Page 76

10 + 4 = 14

14 - 4 = 10

4

Page 78

Across

1. twelve

6. thirteen

7. eleven

Down

2. eight

3. fifteen

4. fourteen

5. ten

Page 79

10

15

5

15

5

Page 80

10 + 5 = 15

15 - 5 = 10

3

Page 82

10

16

6

16

2

Page 83

4

10

14

Page 84

10 + 6 = 16

16 - 6 = 10

7

Page 86

7

14

14

6

Page 87

10

17

7

17

4

Page 88

10 + 7 = 17

17 - 7 = 10

5

Page 90

7

14

17

Page 91

10

18

8

18

4

Page 92

10 + 8 = 18

18 - 8 = 10

2

Page 94

9

8

4

Page 95

10

19

9

19

8

Page 96

10 + 9 = 19

19 - 9 = 10

3

Page 98

10

20

10

20

1

Page 99

5

7

6

Page 100

10 + 10 = 20

20 - 10 = 10

6

Page 101

9

10

2

Made in the USA
Coppell, TX
17 March 2020